Y0-BRO-355

The firemen slide down the pole.

Clang, clang, clang! goes the fire engine bell.

THE LITTLE GOLDEN
FIRE ENGINE BOOK

with pictures by

TIBOR GERGELY

GOLDEN PRESS
Western Publishing Company, Inc.
Racine, Wisconsin

Tenth Printing, 1976

Copyright © 1950, 1959 by Western Publishing Company, Inc.
All rights reserved. Produced in U.S.A.

GOLDEN, A LITTLE GOLDEN BOOK®, and GOLDEN PRESS®
are trademarks of Western Publishing Company, Inc. No part
of this book may be reproduced or copied in any form without
written permission from the publisher.

Ding, ding, ding! goes the alarm.

The chief is on his way.

Here they come!

Watch out! Make way for the hose car.

Hurry, hurry! jump on the hook-and-ladder truck!

The people come running out to see

the great big hook-and-ladder truck.

Here they are at the fire.

The chief tells his men what to do.

Quick! Connect the hoses!

S-s-s-s! goes the water.

Crank, crank. Up go the ladders.

Up go the firemen with their hoses.

Chop, chop, chop! go the axes.

Crash! go the windows.

Down the ladders come the firemen.

They jump into the net to save things from the fire!

Sput, sput, sput! Out goes the fire.

Tired firemen and people go home.

Hurray for the brave firemen!